Margarito's Forest
El Bosque de Don Margarito

by Andy Carter • Ilustrations by Allison Havens

This book is dedicated to:

María Guadalupe Velásquez Tum

Virgilio Vicente

and especially to the children of Saq Ja'.

1

"Papa, I'm tired of climbing and carrying this little tree," cried Esteban.
"How much farther is it to Granny's house?"
Papa smiled. "We are almost there. *Can you see the tall trees up ahead?
They were planted by your great-grandfather, Don Margarito.
The house of your grandmother, Doña Guadalupe, is just beyond this forest.
And you, my son, have shown your strength by carrying this tree all the way up this rocky trail."
"Papa," asked Esteban, "this forest is already so big.
Why are we planting more trees?"
Looking up at the tall trees, Esteban's father replied,
"I think you should ask your Granny. And look
— there she is now, waving to us."

*la kawil apan le nima'q taq che' le k'o aq'an jale' ajsik?

· · · · · · · · · · · · · · · · · · ·

"Papá, estoy cansado de subir cargando este arbolito",
se quejaba Esteban.
"¿Cuánto más falta para llegar a la casa de mi abuelita?"
El papá de Esteban sonrió. "Ya casi llegamos.
*¿Puedes ver los grandes arboles de alla arriba?
Esos los sembró tu bisabuelo, don Margarito.
La casa de tu abuelita, doña Guadalupe, está apenas pasando de este bosque.
Y tú, mijo, has demostrado tu fuerza al cargar este arbolito por todo este camino pedregoso".
"Papá", preguntó Esteban "este bosque ya es muy grande. ¿Por qué estamos
sembrando más árboles?" Mirando hacia los altos árboles, su papá respondió,
"Pienso que deberías preguntarle a tu abuelita. Y mira, -allí está ella ahorita, saludándonos".

3

"Granny, I climbed all the way up to your house today, and I carried this little tree to plant in the forest!" exclaimed Esteban as he carefully handed the tree to Doña Guadalupe. *"My dear Esteban" she said. "Let me look at you. How you've grown!" "Granny," asked Esteban, "why are we planting more trees in Don Margarito's forest?" "Your father is following the traditional ways of the Maya in planting this tree and growing this forest," replied Doña Guadalupe. "Our ways of harmonious living have been passed down from generation to generation. I learned them from my mother and father, just as you are now learning them from your father and me."

* Loq'olaj
WALa
EstebAn

. . . .

"¡Abuelita, yo he subido hoy todo este camino hasta su casa y he traído este arbolito para sembrarlo en el bosque!" dijo Esteban con emoción mientras le entregaba con cuidado el arbolito a doña Guadalupe. *"Mi querido Esteban" dijo ella. "Déjame verte. ¡Cómo has crecido!" "Abuelita", preguntó Esteban "¿Por qué estamos sembrando más árboles en el bosque de don Margarito?" "Tu papá está siguiendo las tradiciones Mayas al sembrar este árbol y así agrandar el bosque", respondió doña Guadalupe. "Nuestras tradiciones de vivir en armonía con la naturaleza han pasado de una generación a otra. Yo las aprendí de mi mamá y de mi papá, así como tú ahora estás aprendiendo de mí y de tu papá".

"But Granny," asked Esteban, "how did Don Margarito learn the Maya ways?"
Doña Guadalupe motioned to Esteban.
*"Come sit beside me and I will tell you about your great-grandfather, Don Margarito.
When he was a child like you, he worked hard in the fields with the other children from
our village. And when the work was done, the others would run and play as children do.
But Margarito did not join them. Instead, he would go exploring in the woodlands.
He liked walking quietly through the tall trees and watching
the playful squirrels leaping from branch to branch.
Margarito's explorations led to many questions about
the woodland's plants and how they grow."

* *

* Sa'j
chatku'l
CHO
nuxkut

"Pero, Abuelita", preguntó Esteban "¿Cómo aprendió don Margarito
las tradiciones Mayas?" Doña Guadalupe llamó a Esteban con un gesto,
*"Ven a sentarte a mi lado y te contaré sobre tu bisabuelo, don Margarito.
Cuando él era niño como tú, trabajaba duro en el campo con otros niños de nuestra comunidad. Y cuando el trabajo terminaba, ellos corrían y jugaban como los niños lo hacen pero Margarito no se juntaba con ellos. En vez de eso, a él le gustaba explorar y andar por los bosques.
Le gustaba caminar tranquilamente entre los altos árboles y mirar las ardillas juguetonas saltan-
do de rama en rama. Estos paseos de Margarito le hicieron pensar
en muchas preguntas sobre las plantas y de cómo éstas crecen".

"These questions drew him to Don Calixto, *the village holy man.
Don Calixto knew the woodlands well because many of the plants he needed for rituals and medicine could only be found there.
He encouraged Margarito's explorations of the woodlands by taking him there to help search for these plants.
He showed Margarito how to move a tree seedling
from the dense underbrush and plant it in a place where it could grow straight and tall.
And while he was still a child,
Margarito began taking seedlings from the woodlands
and planting them on the small plot of land
around his home."

. . . .

*ri ajilonq'ij

"Todas estas preguntas le hicieron buscar a don Calixto,
*el ajilonq'ij, hombre sagrado de nuestra comunidad.
Don Calixto conocía muy bien los bosques porque muchas de las plantas
que él necesitaba para sus ceremonias y para usar como medicina,
únicamente las encontraba ahí. Él inspiró a Margarito en sus exploraciones del bosque, lleván-dolo para ayudar a encontrar esas plantas.
Le enseñó a Margarito cómo trasplantar un arbolito desde el monte
para sembrarlo en un lugar donde pudiera crecer fuerte y alto.
Y mientras todavía era niño, Margarito empezó
a llevar los retoños de los bosques y los sembraba en el terrenito
que estaba alrededor de su casa".

*"as he grew into manhood, Margarito spent more time with Don Calixto learning about the woodlands and the ways of our People. Don Calixto showed Margarito how the woodland's plants live together in harmony. The tall trees provide shade for the low-lying plants. When they die, the low-lying plants become compost and feed the trees. He taught Margarito how to count the days and follow the cycles of the moon, the planets, the stars, and the earth in planting and harvesting. These are the traditional Maya ways that care for the land and respect all of creation. These are the ways Don Margarito followed throughout his life."

. . . .

*Je jas tajin kri'job' uloq xux achi

*"entre mas maduraba, Margarito pasaba más tiempo con don Calixto aprendiendo acerca de los bosques y sobre las tradiciones de nuestra gente. Don Calixto le enseñó a Margarito cómo es que las plantas del bosque viven juntas en armonía. De cómo los árboles más altos les dan sombra a las plantas más pequeñas. Cuando mueren, las plantas pequeñas se convierten en abono y alimentan los árboles. Le enseñó a Margarito a contar los días y a seguir los ciclos de la luna, de los planetas, de las estrellas y de la tierra para sembrar y cosechar. Éstas son las tradiciones Mayas que cuidan de la tierra y respetan toda creación. Éstos son los caminos que don Margarito siguió a lo largo de toda su vida".

Putting Esteban in her lap, Doña Guadalupe continued,
"Let me tell you how I learned our traditional ways
from Don Margarito. I was the first born of his seven children.
* i grew up on this very piece of land
with Mama, Papa, and my sisters and brothers.
Papa's father gave him the land so he could provide for us.
Like the other men in our village, Papa worked hard
to grow enough corn and beans to feed us.
But while other men were clearing more land
to grow their crops, Papa was planting more trees
to grow his forest."

* Tza chi'
xink'iy wi in cho
uwach we
Jun ch'aqap
ulew ri'

. . . .

Poniendo a Esteban sobre sus piernas, doña Guadalupe
continuó, "Déjame contarte cómo aprendí de don Margarito
sobre nuestras tradiciones. Yo fui la primera de sus siete hijos.
* y crecí en este mismo pedazo de tierra
con mi mamá, mi papá, mis hermanas y hermanos.
Mi abuelo le dio estas tierras a mi papá para que pudiera cuidar de nosotros.
Así como los otros hombres de nuestra comunidad,
mi papá trabajaba duro para sembrar suficiente maíz y frijol para alimentarnos. Pero mientras
los otros hombres talaban los árboles del bosque
para tener más tierra para cultivar sus siembras,
mi papá sembraba más árboles para agrandar su bosque".

"When I was old enough, Papa began taking me into the woodlands.
He took a machete, and I carried a cloth sack.
When Papa found a tree seedling or plant he wanted,
he would dig it up with his machete, being careful not to damage
its tender roots. After wrapping the roots and their soil in a piece of cloth,
*he would give them to me to carry in my sack.
"When it was time to plant, Papa would light a candle
to bless the things he planted. He took special care to plant
the seedlings in accordance with his plan for the forest.
He planted them in straight rows, using his machete
to measure the same distance between each seedling."

. . . .

* Are' kuya'
apan chwe in cha'
kink'am uloq
chupam nuchim

"Cuando yo ya era suficientemente grandecito, mi papá
empezó a llevarme al bosque. Él llevaba un machete y yo llevaba
un costal de tela. Cuando mi papá encontraba una planta que le interesaba,
la desenterraba cuidadosamente con su machete para no dañar
sus delicadas raíces. Después de envolver las raíces con tierra en un trapo,
*me las entregaba para que yo las llevara en mi costal.
"Cuando era el momento de sembrarlas, mi papá encendía una candela
para bendecir las cosas que sembraba. Tenía mucho cuidado en el momento de sembrar las
plantitas según su plan para el bosque.
Las sembraba en surcos rectos, usando su machete para medir la misma distancia entre cada
plantita".

15

"But there were some in our village who thought that Papa was strange.
They laughed, 'You have nothing better to do, and that is why
you are always planting trees. Instead of planting trees,
you should be clearing your land to plant more corn and beans.'
"Papa was not bothered by their talk. He told them,
'You laugh and say my trees are not important.
But they are more important than you think.
One day I will have wood for building and cooking.
There will be shady places for the woodland plants to grow.
*this forest is my partnership with the land.
Someday it will benefit my family and many others.'"

. . . .

*We jun
k'iche'laj ri'
are nukchuj in ruk'
ri qanan
uwach ulew

"Pero había algunos de nuestra comunidad que pensaban
que mi papá era extraño. Ellos se reían de él, 'Usted no tiene nada mejor
que hacer y por eso siempre está sembrando árboles.
En vez de sembrar árboles, debería estar preparando su tierra para
sembrar más maíz y más frijol.' "Mi papá no se molestaba por esos comentarios.
Y les decía, 'Ustedes se ríen y dicen que mis árboles no son importantes.
Pero son más importantes de lo que ustedes piensan.
Un día, voy a tener madera para construir y leña para cocinar.
Habrá sombra para que las plantitas del bosque crezcan.
*este bosque es mi aporte a la madre tierra.
Un día beneficiará a mi familia y a muchas otras'".

17

"Even Papa's own father did not understand why Papa was spending so much time planting trees. He worried that we were not getting enough to eat." Esteban asked, "Did you go hungry because Don Margarito was planting so many trees?" "No," replied Doña Guadalupe.

*"besides growing enough corn and beans, Papa was a hunter. He would take his dogs into the woodlands and they would chase an armadillo or a wild boar into its den. Then Papa would build a fire and set up a net at the den's entrance. When smoke filled the den, the animal would come rushing out into the net. Papa knew how to farm and how to hunt. We always had enough to eat."

. . . .

* Ri nutat reta'm xuquje' sak'aj che chapanik

"Incluso el propio papá de mi papá no entendía por qué mi papá pasaba tanto tiempo sembrando árboles. Ya que le preocupaba que no tuviéramos lo suficiente para comer". Esteban le preguntó, "¿Usted alguna vez sufrió hambre porque don Margarito sólo se dedicaba a sembrar árboles?" "No", respondió doña Guadalupe.

*"Aparte de sembrar suficiente maíz y frijol, mi papá era cazador. Llevaba sus perros a los bosques para perseguir armadillos o coches de monte hasta dar con sus cuevas. Y luego, mi papá encendía fuego y ponía una red en la entrada de la cueva. Cuando la cueva se llenaba de humo, el animalito salía corriendo y quedaba atrapado en la red. Mi papá sabía sembrar y cazar. Por eso, siempre tuvimos lo suficiente para comer".

"As we were growing up,
Papa would take me and my brothers into the woodlands.
He showed us where to look for the plants we could eat
and herbs we could use. He would pick a few leaves or dig up a root
and make us taste it. He told us to look closely at the plant's leaves
and remember its taste, because someday we might need it.
"As a child, I did not pay enough attention to Papa.
But there came a time when *i was hiding in the jungle
with my two young children. We were hungry and I began
remembering the things Papa taught us.
We survived by eating weeds and roots."

* Le in tajin
kink'u' wib'
xe taq nim
k'iche'laj

. . . .

"Mientras crecíamos, mi papá nos llevaba a mí
y a mis hermanos al bosque. Nos enseñaba dónde buscar las plantas
que podíamos comer y las hierbas que podíamos utilizar.
Él cortaba algunas hojas o escarbaba una raíz y nos las hacía probar.
Nos decía que observáramos cuidadosamente las hojas de las plantas
y que recordáramos su sabor porque algún un día las podríamos necesitar.
"Como niña, yo no le prestaba suficiente atención a mi papá.
Pero hubo una vez en mi vida *cuando me estaba escondiendo
en la jungla con mis dos hijos. Teníamos hambre
y empecé a recordar las cosas que mi papá nos había enseñado.
Sobrevivimos comiendo hierbas y raíces".

"Granny," cried Esteban,
"when were you living in the jungle and why were you
eating weeds and roots?"
"While your father was still a baby,
*the army came and destroyed our village.
They burnt our homes down to the ground
and they dug up our crops. I was shot.
A bullet went through my arm and I fled into the jungle
with your father and his sister.
All we had was the clothes on our backs,"
replied Doña Guadalupe.

chajil
taq amaq' tza
xkik'is tzij
pa uwi' qakomon

. . . .

"Abuelita", preguntó Esteban,
"¿Cuándo vivió usted en la jungla
y por qué estaba comiendo hierbas y raíces?"
"Cuando tu papá todavía era bebé,
*el ejercito vino y destruyo' nuestra comunidad.
Ellos quemaron nuestras casas y destruyeron nuestras cosechas.
A mí me dispararon.
Una bala me traspasó un brazo y huí a la jungla
con tu padre y su hermana.
Todo lo que teníamos era la ropa que llevábamos encima",
respondió doña Guadalupe.

23

*"and while we were living in the jungle,
I used what I had learned from Papa.
Knowing which plants we could eat kept us from starving.
Knowing which plants we could use as medicine kept us healthy.
 "The day we left, I pleaded with Papa to come with us,
but he would not leave his home and the forest he loved.
After that, I never saw Papa again.
It was a terrible time for our village and many others
throughout our land. When you are a little older,
I will tell you more about those days
and the dirty war that tore us apart."

* are chi'
ujk'o
pa kim tak
k'iche'laj

. . . .

**"y mientras vivi'amos en la jungla,
yo usaba lo que había aprendido de mi papá.
El saber qué plantas podíamos comer nos salvó de morir de hambre.
El saber qué plantas podíamos usar como medicina nos mantuvo sanos.
"El dia que nos fuimos, le rogué a mi papá que se fuera con nosotros,
pero él no quería dejar su hogar ni el bosque que tanto amaba.
Después de eso, nunca volví a ver otra vez a mi papá.
Cuando seas mayorcito te contaré más sobre aquellos días
y sobre la trágica guerra que nos separó".

"But today I want you to remember Don Margarito.
Although the war took him away from us, his spirit lives on in this forest.
The trees he planted have grown tall. They have given us firewood
for our stoves and lumber for rebuilding our community.
They provide shade for the woodland plants.
My neighbors come to enjoy this beautiful forest and all it has to offer."
"And Granny," said Esteban, "this tree I carried all the way up the mountain, can we plant
it now?"
"Yes, my dear Esteban," smiled Doña Guadalupe.
* "We will light a candle and I will show you the Maya way
of planting just as Papa showed me, so many years ago."

. . . .

"Pero hoy quiero que recuerdes a don Margarito. Aunque la guerra
lo separó de nosotros, su espíritu sigue viviendo en este bosque.
Los árboles que él sembró han crecido tan altos.
Y nos han dado leña para nuestra cocina y madera para reconstruir
nuestra comunidad. Nos dan sombra para las plantas del bosque.
Los vecinos vienen a disfrutar y a utilizar todo lo que nos ofrece
este hermoso bosque". "Y abuelita", dijo Esteban, "este árbol que cargué hasta la montaña, ¿lo
podemos sembrar ahorita?"
"Sí mi querido Esteban", dijo doña Guadalupe sonriendo.
* "Encenderemos una candela y te enseñaré la costumbre Maya de sembrar,
tal y como mi papá me enseñó a mí, hace muchos años".

About This Book, by Andy Carter

Margarito's Forest is based on the life of Don Margarito Esteban Álvarez Velázquez as told by his daughter, Dona' María Guadalupe. This story of the Maya Cosmovision, passed from one generation to the next is set in Saq Ja', a small, remote village in the mountains of central Guatemala. Saq Ja' was settled early in the twentieth century by indigenous Maya who left the highland plains because of deforestation and overcrowding. For many decades the families that settled in Saq Ja' grew and prospered. And it was there that Don Margarito—was born on October 18, 1931.

The peaceful existence of the families in Saq Ja' began to crumble in 1954, when a military coup overthrew Jacobo Árbenz Guzmán, the democratically elected president of Guatemala. The overthrow led to a series of military dictators and a long dirty war, which included genocide of the Maya. In a series of assaults between 1981 and 1982, the village of Saq Ja' was destroyed by the Guatemalan military. Many villagers died in the attacks, while others joined the political resistance, fled into the mountains, or went to refugee camps in Central America. Among those who went into hiding was María Guadalupe and among those who fled Guatemala was Virgilio Vicente. In response to this humanitarian crisis, the Sanctuary Movement was formed in the 1980s to welcome Central American refugees into the United States. In 1986 Don Virgilio was taken into sanctuary at University Church in Chicago, Illinois.

After the signing of the Guatemalan Peace Accords in 1996, some of those displaced by the war began to return to their ancestral lands. In 1998, accompanied by members of University Church, Don Virgilio returned to participate in the rebuilding of Saq Ja'. With that pilgrimage and Don Virgilio's wise leadership, a partnership was established between the people of Saq Ja' and members of University Church. Almost every year since that initial trip in 1998, a delegation from University Church has returned to Saq Ja'.

In April of 2007 I made my first trip to Guatemala as a member of the University Church delegation. On our last day In Saq Ja', Don Virgilio took the delegation on a tour of various projects in the community. Since it was hot, he took us to a cool, densely forested area to sit and talk. At that time I was struck by the stark contrast between the lush old-growth forest where we sat, and the fields and scrub brush that surrounded it. I asked Don Virgilio if he knew anything about this forest. He told me that Margarito, a man with a peculiar love of trees, had planted the forest. He added that although Margarito was killed during the war, his daughter, María Guadalupe, was now living here and tending

About the Illustrations

his forest. With this intriguing introduction, and a series of interviews with María Guadalupe, the development of Margarito's Forest was begun.

During the war years María Guadalupe lost most of her family and was forced to flee from Saq Ja' with her two young children. Following the Peace Accords, she returned to Saq Ja', where she has continued Don Margarito's legacy of community and ecological leadership. This book is a commemoration of her courage and the preservation Margarito's forest. As the devastating effects of climate change become clear, Don Margarito's life and the Cosmovision of the Maya offer timely wisdom for a planet in peril.

The illustrations for *Margarito's Forest* are by Allison Havens. Originally from Chicago, in the US, Allison currently lives and works in Xela, Guatemala. The illustrations are a mixture of her original drawings and paintings collaged together with photos, traditional Guatemalan textiles, and artwork by the children of the Saq Ja' elementary school.

She spent two sessions with the children in the Saq Ja' community drawing local animals and plants as well as specific scenes to accompany the text.

"Maria Guadalupe in Margarito's Forest with the children during one of the workshops."

29

Acknowledgments

This book would not have been possible without the courage and determination of María Guadalupe Velásquez Tum and the people of Saq Ja'. I am deeply grateful to María Guadalupe for inviting me into her home and sharing her father's story. I am also grateful to the people of Saq Ja' for their hospitality and support for this project. I want to give a special thanks to the school teachers at Saq Ja' elementary school who have collaborated on this project and to the school's students who have contributed their drawings for the illustrations.

In all five of my trips with University Church delegations to Guatemala, I have received assistance and enthusiastic encouragement from fellow delegates in sharing Margarito's story. But whatever success *Margarito's Forest* may achieve, it must be shared equally with Allison Havens. Besides her amazing illustrations, I am especially grateful to Allison for her capable management of the many aspects of this project. I also want to express my appreciation to Omar Mejía, Manuel Hernández, and Eduardo Elías for their fine work on the Spanish and K'iche' translations.

Throughout the project Garry Sparks has lead me to a deeper appreciation of Maya culture and spirituality. He has also provided detailed feedback on texts and translations. Several other people have read and provided helpful comments on the story as it has evolved. These include Carol Saller, Bill Ayers, Ava Belisle-Chatterjee, Dan Dale, Hal Havens and Santos Par. Besides reading and commenting on each of its many versions, my wife, Diane Herrmann, has patiently supported me each step of the way to the completion of *Margarito's Forest.*

Andy Carter, February 2016

STUDY QUESTIONS FOR TEACHERS, LIBRARIAN AND PARENTS

1. Dona' Guadalupe told Esteban that caring for the land and respecting all of creation were the traditional ways of the Maya. She said she had learned these traditional ways from her father, Don Margarito. What are some important things that you have learned from your parents?

2. As a child Margarito liked to go exploring in the woodlands to find new and interesting plants and animals. Where do you like to go exploring? What discoveries have you made in these places?

3. Margarito's questions about plants and animals led him to the village holy man, Don Calixto. When you have questions, where do you go to find answers?

4. Don Calixto taught Margarito how to count the days and follow the cycles of the earth in planting and harvesting. Why do you think the ancient Maya needed to count the days? How do you think the Maya learned to predict the cycles of the seasons? What in nature can you use to tell things about the seasons?

5. When the army came to destroy Dona' Guadalupe's village, she fled into the jungle with her two young children. But Don Margarito would not leave his land, and he was killed. Throughout history there have been people with the courage to die for what they believe. Can you think of any other people in history who have been willing to die for their beliefs?

6. When Dona' Guadalupe fled into the jungle with her two young children, they survived by eating weeds and roots. How did she know which plants she could eat? Do you know any wild plants that you can eat?

7. People in the village laughed at Margarito for planting trees instead of planting more corn and beans. But he was not bothered by their teasing because he believed that his forest was important. Have you ever been teased or taunted by someone who did not agree with what you were doing?

8. When Dona' Guadalupe and Esteban planted his seedling, they lit a candle to ask the Earth's blessing. Lighting a candle when planting was a Maya ritual that Dona' Guadalupe learned from her father. Does your family have any rituals?

9. The Mayan people hold a deep love and respect for the land. If we adopted the Maya deep respect for the land, how would we live differently in our community?

10. Why is it important to plant and care for forests? What do they contribute to our lives or to the condition of planet earth? If you would like to learn more about trees you can go to this website:http://extension.illinois.edu/trees1/16.html

Here is a fun scavenger hunt activity that you can do with your class:http://ellenjmchenry.co/botany-scavenger-hunt/

EXAMPLES OF MAYA LANGUAGE

This book uses three different languages. The text of the story is in English and Spanish. In the margin of each page between the English and Spanish text is a caption taken from the story that is written in K'iche'. K'iche' is the indigenous Mayan language spoken in Margarito's village. The captions also appear in the English text and the Spanish text. The captions are written in green so you can see the same words in all three languages.

MAYAN NUMBERS

In this book you will notice that besides the familiar Arabic number system that we use every day (1...2..3..), there are also groups of dots and lines at the bottom of most pages. These dots and lines are Mayan numerals. Mayan numerals are written using only three symbols: zero, represented as a shell shape; one, a dot; and five, a bar. Look at the bottom right hand corner of page number seven, and find the bar with two dots above it. Can you see how this represents the number seven?

While the Mayan numerals look very different from our Arabic numerals, there is one important similarity. Both systems use zero as a placeholder. You may be asking yourself what's a placeholder? Think about the number 20 and what the zero tells you in this number. The zero is a placeholder in 20 because it puts 2 in the tens place making the numeral 20 stands for 2 tens. So zero is a very special number that means much more than nothing. The Maya were one of the world's first civilizations to use zero as a place holder. They began using zero around 350 CE.

An interesting difference between the two number systems is that the Arabic system is base 10 while the Mayan system is base 20. Can you think of a reason that an ancient civilization might have chosen 10 or 20 as a basis for its counting system? In the Arabic system there are 10 numerals from 0 to 9. The number that follows 9 is 10 which uses 0 as a placeholder to put a 1 in the ten's place.

The Maya used a vertical base 20 place value number system. Look for the Mayan number on page 21 to see how this works. There is one dot above another. The dot on top stands for one 20 and the dot below it stands for one 1. Now look on the previous page and see if you can find the shell-like symbol for zero in the Mayan number 20.

If you would like to know more about the Maya number system, go to this link:

http://www.basic-mathematics.com/mayan-numeration-system.html

CHILDREN'S BOOKS from HARD BALL PRESS

Joelito's Big Decision, La gran Decisión de Joelito:
Ann Berlak (Author), Daniel Camacho (Illustrator),
José Antonio Galloso (Translator)

Manny and the Mango Tree, Many y el Árbol de Mango:
Alí R. and Valerie Bustamante (Authors), Monica Lunot-Kuker (Illustrator). Mauricio Niebla (Translator)

The Cabbage That Came Back:
Stephen Pearl & Rafael Pearl (Authors), Rafael Pearl (Illustrator), Sara Pearl (Translator)

Hats Off For Gabbie, ¡Aplausos para Gaby!:
Marivir Montebon (Author), Yana Podriez (Illustrator),
Mauricio Niebla (Translator)

Margarito's Forest/El Bosque de Don Margarito:
Andy Carter (Author), Alison Havens (Illustrator), Sergio Villatoro (Graphic Design),
Artwork contributions by the children of the Saq Ja' elementary school
K'iche tranlations by Eduardo Elas and Manuel Hernandez
Translated by Omar Mejia

Jimmy's Carwash Adventure, Jimmy Carwash Aventura:
Victor Narro (Author & Translator),
Yana Podriez (Illustrator), Laura Flores (Translator)

HOW TO ORDER BOOKS:

Order books from www.hardballpress.com, Amazon.com,
or independent booksellers everywhere.
**Receive a 20% discount for orders of 10 or more,
a 40% discount for orders of 50 or more when ordering
from www.hardballpress.com.**

CPSIA information can be obtained
at www.ICGtesting.com
Printed in the USA
LVOW06*1342081017

551658LV00017B/167/P